HENRY
3

JAMES
5

PERCY
D1112853

MEET ALL THESE FRIENDS IN BUZZ BOOKS:

Thomas the Tank Engine
The Animals of Farthing Wood
Biker Mice From Mars
James Bond Junior
Joshua Jones
Fireman Sam
Rupert
Babar

First published 1990 by Buzz Books
an imprint of Reed Children's Books
Michelin House, 81 Fulham Road, London, SW3 6RB
and Auckland, Melbourne, Singapore and Toronto
Reprinted 1993, 1994

Photographs by David Mitton, Kenny McArthur and
Terry Permane for Britt Allcroft's production of
Thomas the Tank Engine and Friends.
ISBN 1 85591 007 1
Printed in Italy by Olivotto

JAMES AND THE TROUBLESOME TRUCKS
buzz books

James had not seen the Fat Controller for some time. Not since the day when he had nearly lost his red coat and been painted blue instead.

That was the time when James had been very naughty. First he had let off steam and sprayed water on the Fat Controller's new top-hat. Then he had run too fast and made a hole in one of the coaches. The driver had to mend the hole with newspaper and a passenger's bootlace. The Fat Controller had been very angry.

Now James was alone in the shed. He was not even allowed out to push coaches and trucks in the yard.

At last the Fat Controller arrived and came to see him.

"I can see that you are sorry, James," he said. "I hope now that you will be a better engine. You have given me a lot of trouble," said the Fat Controller. "People are laughing at my railway, and I do not like it at all."

James said that he was very sorry and promised to be a better engine.

The Fat Controller said, "I want you to pull some trucks for me."

James was delighted and puffed away.

"Here are your trucks, James," said Thomas the Tank Engine. "Have you got some bootlaces ready?" Thomas ran off, laughing.

"Oh! Oh! Oh!" said the trucks. "We want a proper engine, not a red monster."

But James took no notice and started as soon as the guard was ready.

"Come along, come along," he puffed. But the trucks were being naughty.

"We won't! We won't!" they screamed.

James took no notice and he pulled the screeching trucks sternly out of the station and onto the line.

The trucks tried very hard to make James give up, but he still kept on. Sometimes their brakes would slip on, and sometimes their axles would run hot.

Each time the trouble had to be put right, and each time, James would start again. But he was not going to let them beat him.

"Give up! Give up! You can't pull us," shouted the trucks.

But James puffed on, and slowly he pulled them along the line.

At last they saw Gordon's hill. This was the famous place where Gordon, the big proud engine, had once got stuck! Little Edward, one of the Tender Engines, had had to push Gordon up the hill!

As James came nearer to the hill, his driver warned him to be careful and to look out for trouble from the trucks.

"We'll go fast and get them up the hill before they know it," the driver whispered to James. "Don't let them stop you."

So James went faster and faster and soon they were half-way up the hill.

"I'm doing it! I'm doing it!" he panted. "Will the top ever come?"

Then with a sudden jerk, it all became much easier. James thought it was over and that he had pulled the trucks to the top of the hill without any trouble. But his driver shut off steam.

"They've done it again," he said. "We've left our tail behind. Look!"

The last trucks were running backwards down the hill. The coupling had broken. But the guard stopped the trucks and climbed out to warn other engines.

"That's why it was so easy," said James, as he backed the other trucks carefully down the hill. "What silly things trucks are. There might have been an accident."

Edward had come along. He offered to help, but James had decided that *he* was going to pull these trucks by himself.

"Good," said Edward. "Don't let them beat you!"

James struggled slowly up the hill. He pulled and puffed as hard as he could. After a long time he finally pulled the trucks to the top.

"I've done it! I've done it!" he cried, and his driver cheered.

They reached the station safely and James was resting in the yard when Edward pulled up.

"Peep, peep!" he whistled.

Then James saw the Fat Controller. He thought that he would be in trouble. But the Fat Controller was smiling. He had been in Edward's train and he had seen everything.

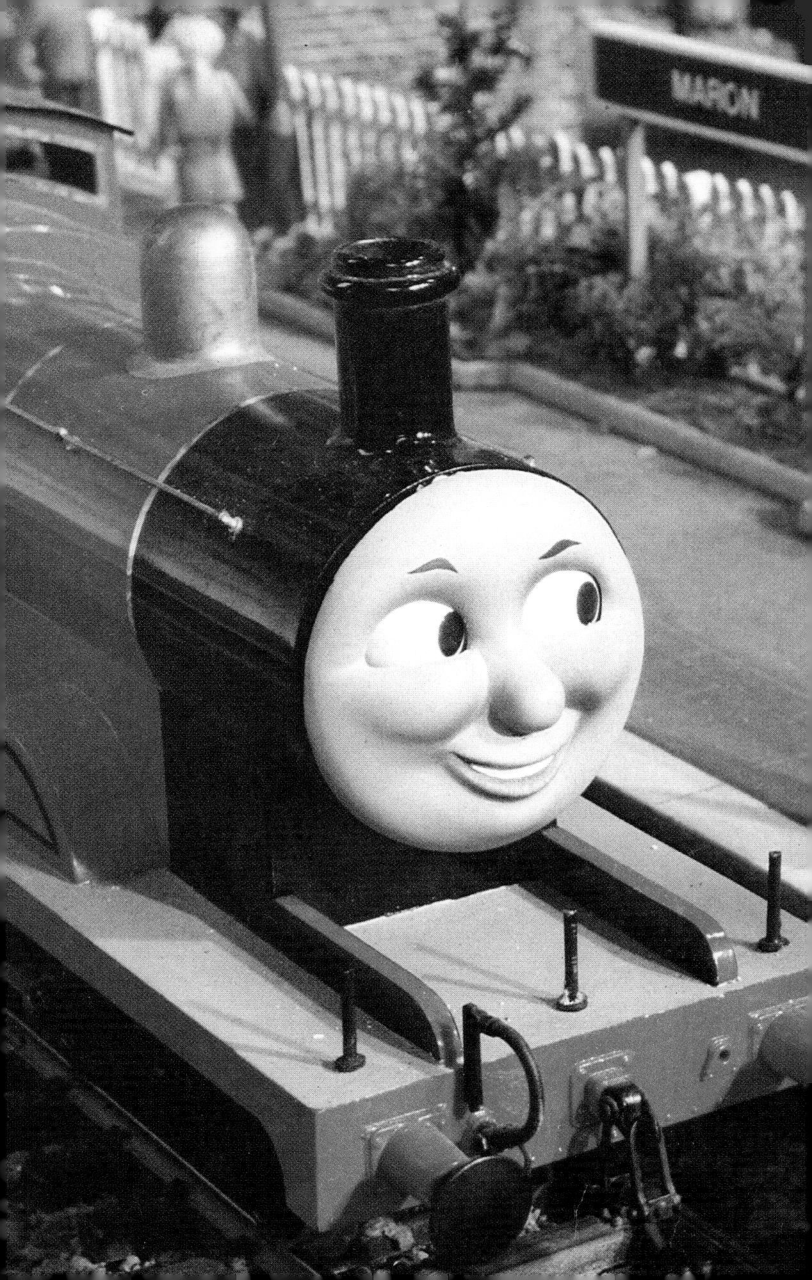
MARON

"You've made the most troublesome trucks on the line behave," he said. "After that, you deserve to keep your red coat!"

THOMAS
1

EDWARD
2

GORDON
4